My Life in the Wild
Cheetah

writer **Meredith Costain**   illustrator **Mick Posen**

KINGFISHER

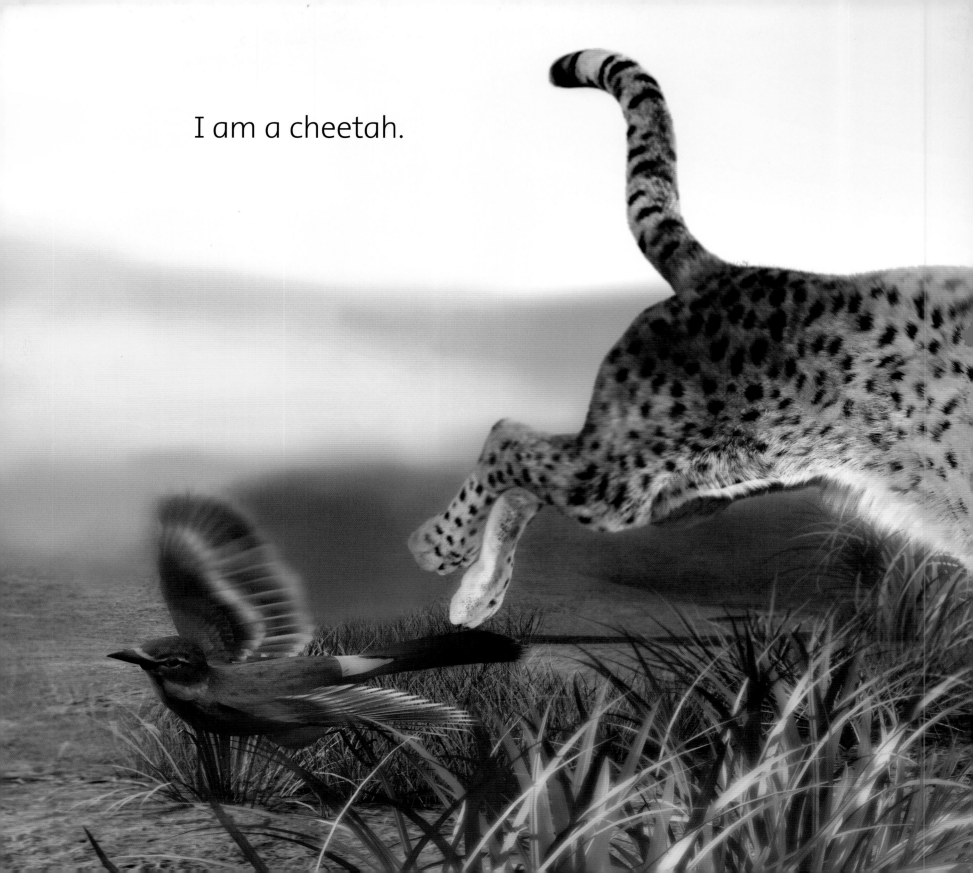

I am a cheetah.

I have a lean body with black spots and 'tear stripes' on my face. My home is the African grasslands. I run as fast as the wind. Let me tell you my story.

My brothers and I are born. I cannot see
my mother yet but I can smell her. I snuggle
into her warm tummy, drinking her milk.
She licks my wriggly brother clean
with her raspy tongue.

Each day I grow stronger and bigger.
My teeth grow longer and sharper.
But there are other animals on the prowl,
sniffing around, looking for dinner. Our mother
moves us around from place to place to keep us safe.

Every few days our mother leaves us
to go hunting. We stay in our nest, cuddled
together, our tummies rumbling with hunger.

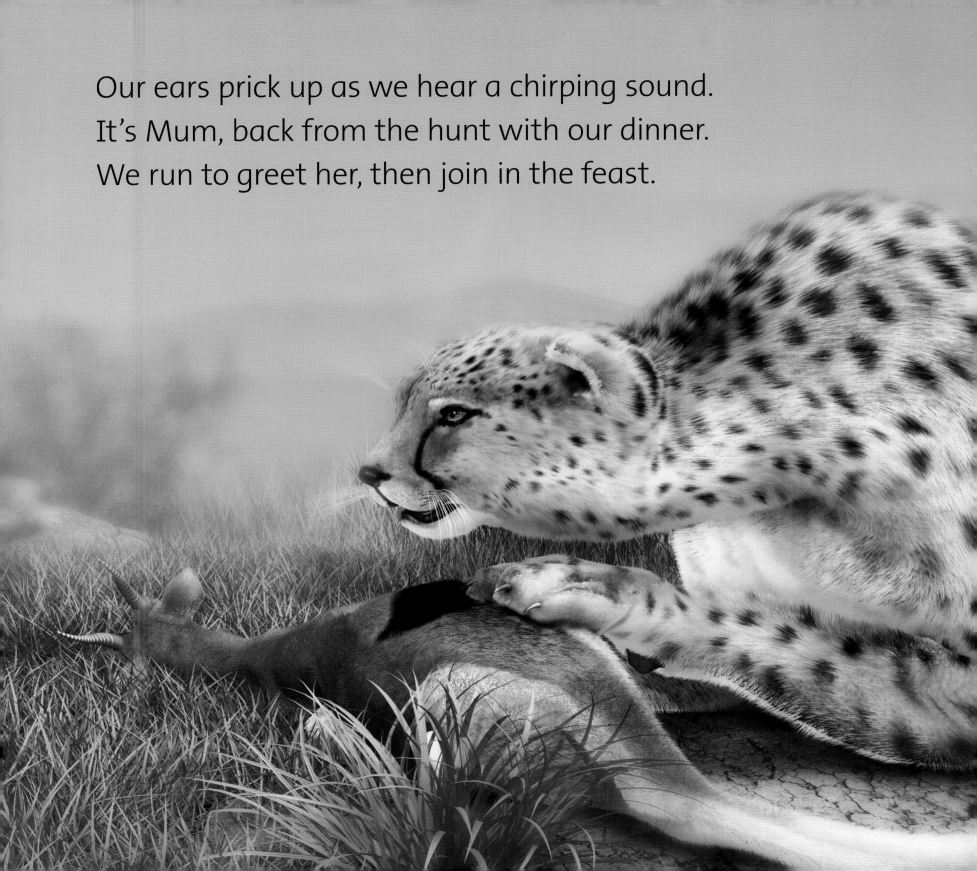

Our ears prick up as we hear a chirping sound.
It's Mum, back from the hunt with our dinner.
We run to greet her, then join in the feast.

Learning to hunt is fun! We play together every day, pouncing and jumping and tripping each other up. We box and wrestle and play tug-of-war.

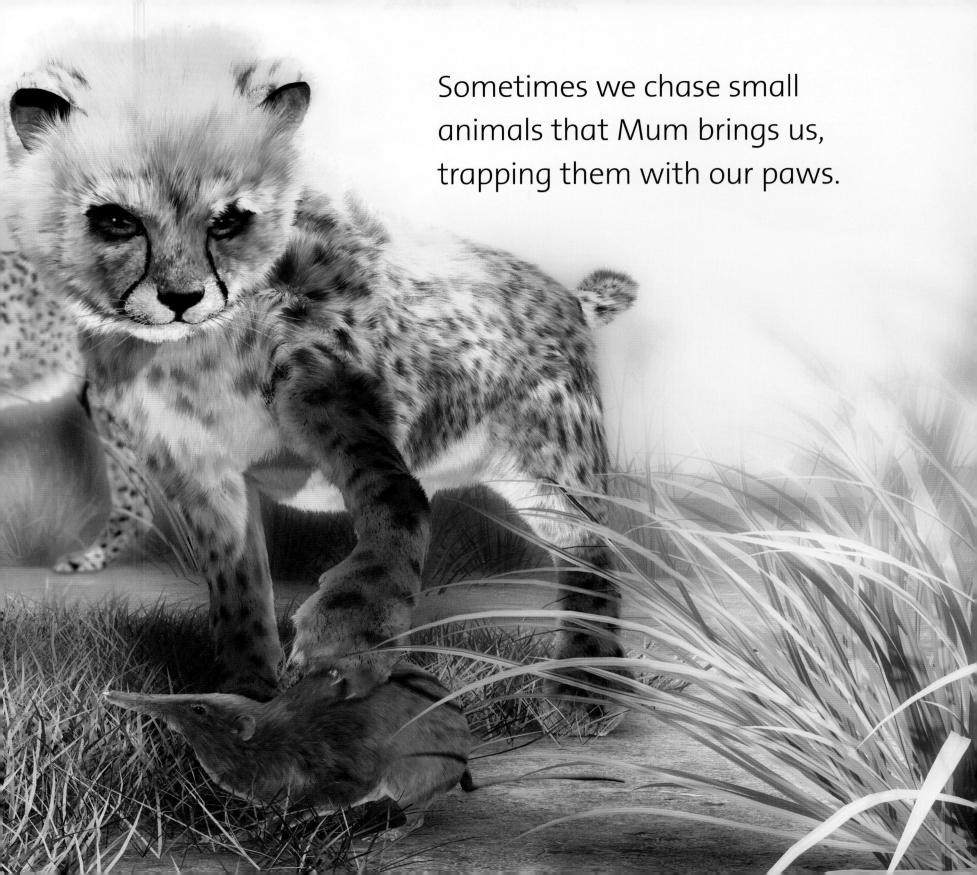

Sometimes we chase small animals that Mum brings us, trapping them with our paws.

It's time for our first hunt. We follow
our mother as she patiently stalks
a herd of wildebeest, but we
soon lose interest.

My brothers start to play fight. Their noise alerts the animal our mother has chosen. It takes off across the plains. Mum speeds after it, then falls back, exhausted. The wildebeest escapes — for now.

The next day it's my turn. I choose a small gazelle, away from its herd. Then I wait. And watch.

I slink forwards. The gazelle lifts its head
and sniffs the air. I freeze. Then, slowly,
silently, I creep towards it again.
Closer . . . closer . . . until finally . . .

I pounce! The gazelle leaps in fright,
then bounds away, zigzagging across
the grassy plain. I twist and turn
as I dash after it, trying my best
not to trip or fall.

Then I bring it down with
a swipe of my paw.

I lie in the grass, puffing and panting.
I'm too tired to eat right now. I drag
the gazelle back to our den.

Later, three hungry hyenas come sniffing around. My mother helps my brothers to chase them away.

Time passes. Our mother moves on to a new hunting ground, leaving us to look after ourselves. My brothers and I still practise our charging and pouncing. I am the fastest runner,

and the best hunter!

It is time for me
to leave my brothers.
They will stay together,
helping each other to hunt.
I set out across the wide plains,
looking for a hunting ground of my own.

I have found a new home, far away from my old one.
I saw my mother once, chasing a gazelle.
But I never saw my brothers again.

These days, I don't have time
to play. Now I have my own family,
it's time for me to teach
them all to hunt!

Did You Know?

Cheetahs usually give birth to three to five cubs.

First they make a nest for their cubs, in a quiet, hidden spot, such as tall grass. Cubs are blind when they are born. They begin crawling around the nest at four to ten days, when their eyes finally open. Before then, they use touch and scent to find their mother's milk.

The mother cheetah moves her cubs for safety.

The mother hides her cubs in long grass, under bushes or among rocks while she goes off to hunt. Every few days she moves her cubs to a different place, so their scent does not build up and attract predators.

Cheetahs make many different sounds.

A mother calling her cubs gives a high-pitched, birdlike chirp, which can be heard from far away. Cheetahs also use this sound when greeting each other. They purr like a cat when content, bleat when in distress and growl or hiss when attacking or defending themselves.

Cubs prepare for life by playing.

Cubs learn how to hunt for themselves through play. They practise pouncing, stalking and ambushing each other, or small animals their mother brings them. Playing also helps them to grow stronger and move their bodies well.

Cheetahs can run fast, but not for long.

A cheetah can only sprint for about 30 seconds before it runs out of energy. If its prey can stay out of reach for that long, it may be able to escape. Only about half of a cheetah's chases are successful.

Cheetahs choose and stalk their prey.

Cheetahs move almost silently when they are hunting. This allows them to get as close to their prey as they can before starting the chase. They look out for an animal that is small, weak, old or separated from the herd, to increase their chances of catching it.

Did You Know? (continued)

The fastest animal on land is the cheetah.

Cheetahs are built for speed, with lean bodies, flexible spines and hips, and large, strong hearts and lungs. Their short, blunt claws grip the ground as they run, like the spikes on a pair of running shoes. Having a long tail helps them to keep their balance during sharp turns.

After hunting, cheetahs can be too exhausted to eat.

Once they have caught their prey, cheetahs are often too tired to eat right away. Instead, they hide it in a safe place. If undisturbed by vultures, hyenas or lions, cheetahs can spend the whole day eating.

The mother cheetah moves on to start a new family.

The mother leaves her cubs when they are about 18 months old, to start another family. The cubs stay together for about another six months, practising their hunting skills.

Male and female cheetahs live separately.

Female cheetahs leave their male siblings at around two years of age and set up their own territory, called the 'home range'. The males stay together in small groups for the rest of their lives.

The cheetah's tail has spots, black rings and a white tip.

When moving her cubs through long grass, the mother cheetah raises her tail. Its bright white tip acts as a marker to help the cubs keep her in sight.

Meet the Cat Family

Cheetahs are part of the cat family.
Here are some other family members.

Jaguar

Lion cubs are born
with brown spots on
their bodies, which fade
as they grow older.

Pride of lions

Serval

QUIZ

1. How many different kinds of cats
   can you see here?

2. Which cat has a mane?

3. Which cat has the most stripes?

4. Which cat has a small head
   and large ears?

Cheetah

Scientific name: *Acinonyx jubatus*

Coat colour: tan with black spots, and a white belly

Body length: 122 centimetres

Weight: 31–63 kilograms

Shoulder height: 76+ centimetres

Tail length: 72 centimetres

Top speed: 112 kilometres per hour

Acceleration: 0 to 84 kilometres per hour in 3 seconds

Conservation status: endangered

Habitat: small pockets of Africa

Where cheetahs live

AFRICA

Margay

Tiger

Lynx

5. How many have long tails?

6. How many have short tails?

7. Which of these cats looks the most like a cheetah?

8. Which cat has tufts on its ears?

Glossary

ambush	to hide, then attack
cub	a baby of a cheetah or other large cat
escape	to get away from danger
exhausted	very tired
mane	longer hair along the neck or head
predator	an animal that hunts
prey	an animal hunted as food
pride	a family or group of lions
sibling	a brother or sister
sprint	to quickly run a short distance
stalk	to follow quietly and secretly
territory	area where a group of animals lives

First published 2011 by Kingfisher
an imprint of Macmillan Children's Books
a division of Macmillan Publishers Limited
20 New Wharf Road, London N1 9RR
Basingstoke and Oxford

Associated companies throughout the world
www.panmacmillan.com

A CIP catalogue record for this book is available
from the British Library.

Conceived and produced by
Weldon Owen Pty Ltd
59–61 Victoria Street, McMahons Point
Sydney NSW 2060, Australia
weldonowenpublishing.com

Copyright © 2011 Weldon Owen Pty Ltd

WELDON OWEN PTY LTD

Managing Director Kay Scarlett
Publisher Corinne Roberts
Creative Director Sue Burk
**Senior Vice President,
International Sales** Stuart Laurence
Sales Manager, North America Ellen Towell
**Administration Manager,
International Sales** Kristine Ravn

Editor Shan Wolody
Consultant Professor Phil Whitfield
Design Concept Cooling Brown Ltd
Designers Gabrielle Green, Adam Walker
Design Assistant Emily Spencer
Images Manager Trucie Henderson
Production Director Todd Rechner
Production and Prepress Controller Mike Crowton
Illustrations Mick Posen/The Art Agency
except Meet the Cat Family pages.

ISBN: 978-0-7534-3379-9

Printed and bound in China by 1010 Printing Int Ltd.

The paper used in the manufacture of this book is
sourced from wood grown in sustainable forests.
It complies with the Environmental Management
System Standard ISO 14001:2004

A WELDON OWEN PRODUCTION